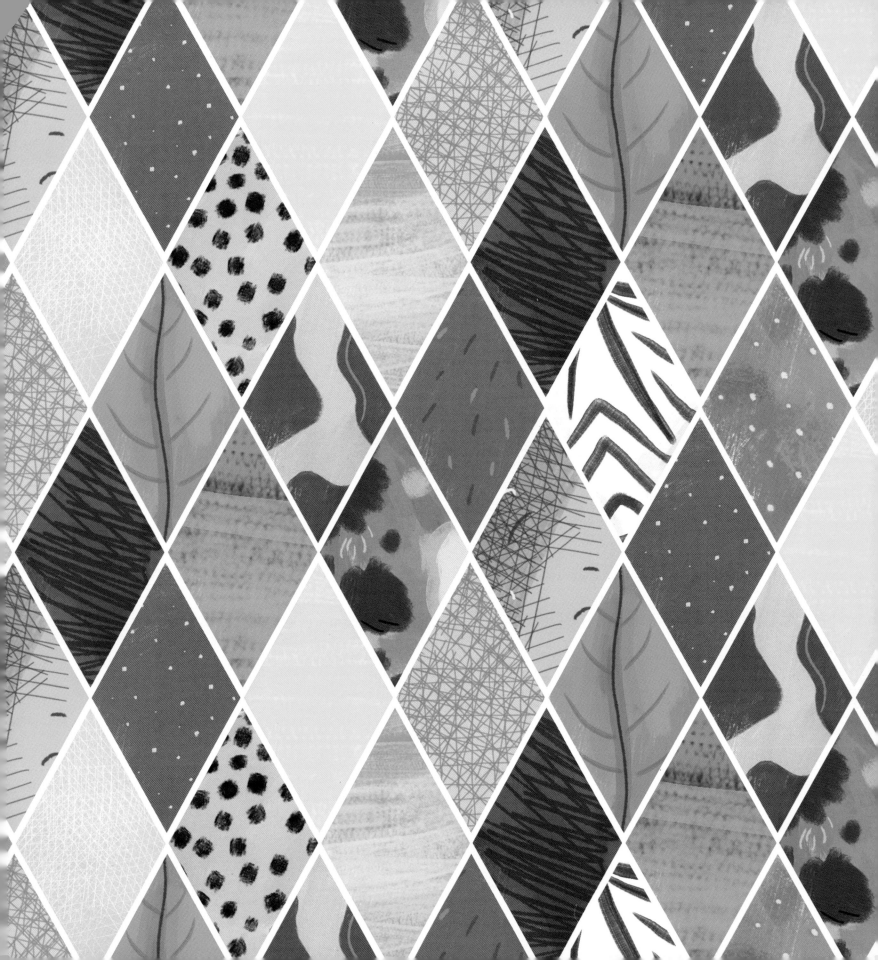

IMAGINE THAT™

Licensed exclusively to Imagine That Publishing Ltd
Tide Mill Way, Woodbridge, Suffolk, IP12 1AP, UK
www.imaginethat.com
Copyright © 2023 Imagine That Group Ltd
All rights reserved
0 2 4 6 8 9 7 5 3 1
Manufactured in China

Retold by Pip Williams
Illustrated by Richard Watson

ISBN 978-1-80105-581-9

A catalogue record for this book is available from the British Library

If You're Snappy and You Know It!

SNAP!

Retold by
Pip Williams

Illustrated by
Richard Watson

If you're snappy and you know it,
Snap your teeth!

If you're swishy and you know it,
Swish your tail!

SWISH!

SWISH!

If you're swishy and you know it,
And you really want to show it,
If you're swishy and you know it,
Swish your tail!

SWISH!

If you're wiggly and you know it,
Wiggle your bottom!

WIGGLE!
WIGGLE!

If you're wiggly and you know it,
Wiggle your bottom!

If you're wiggly and you know it,
And you really want to show it,
If you're wiggly and you know it,
Wiggle your bottom!

WIGGLE!

WIGGLE!

If you're flappy and you know it,
Flap your ears!

If you're flappy and you know it,
And you really want to show it,
If you're flappy and you know it,
Flap your ears!

FLAP!

FLAP!

If you're stompy and you know it,
Stomp your feet!

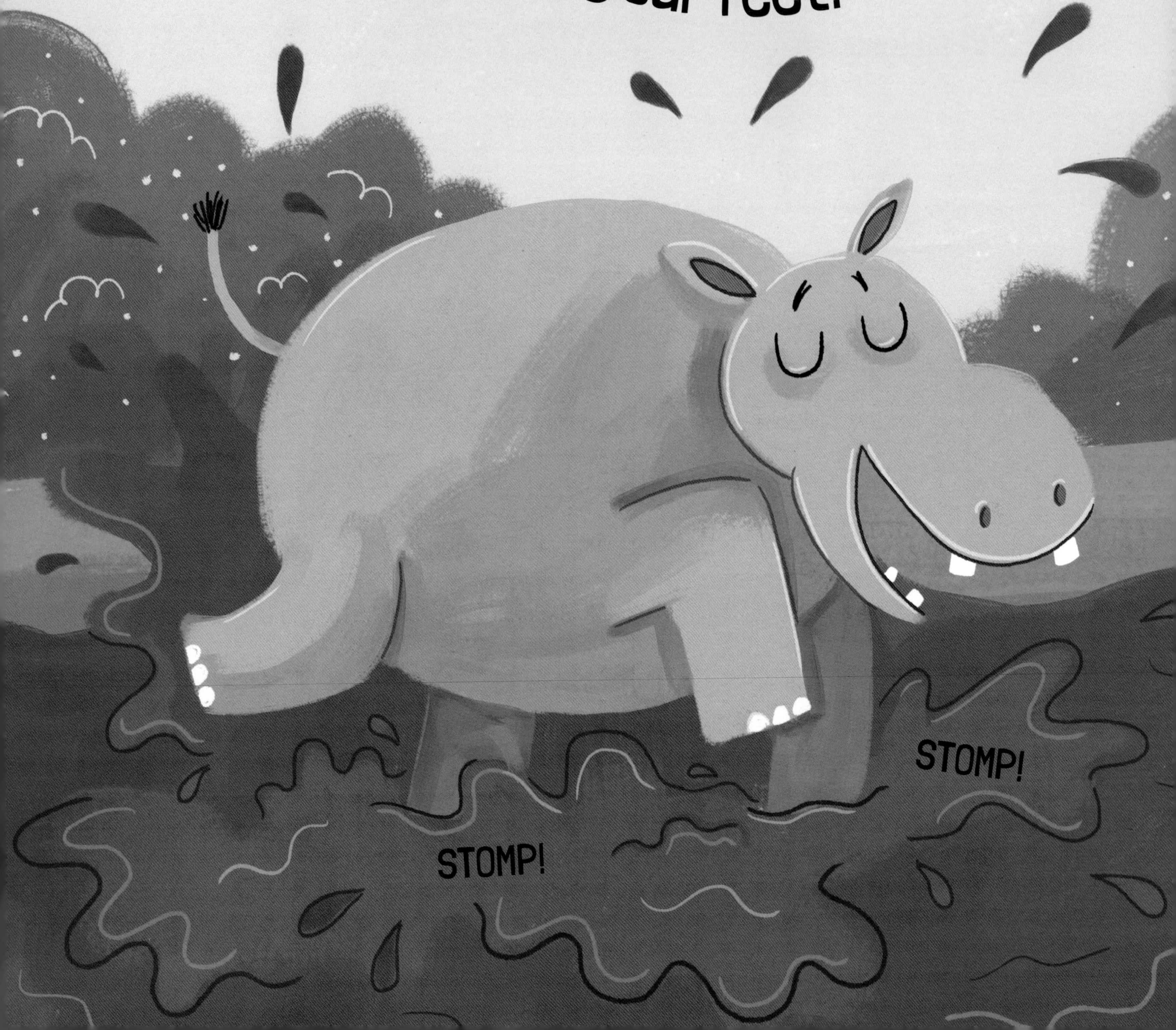

If you're stompy and you know it,
Stomp your feet!

If you're stompy and you know it,
And you really want to show it,
If you're stompy and you know it,
Stomp your feet!

STOMP!

STOMP!

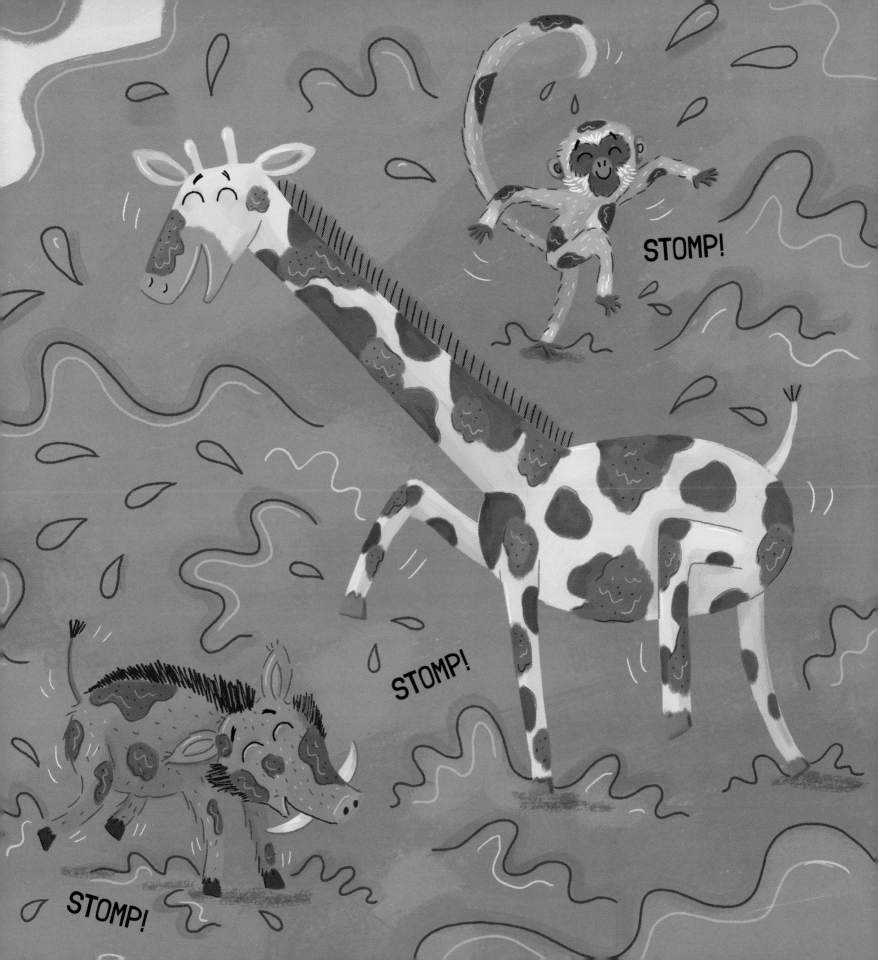

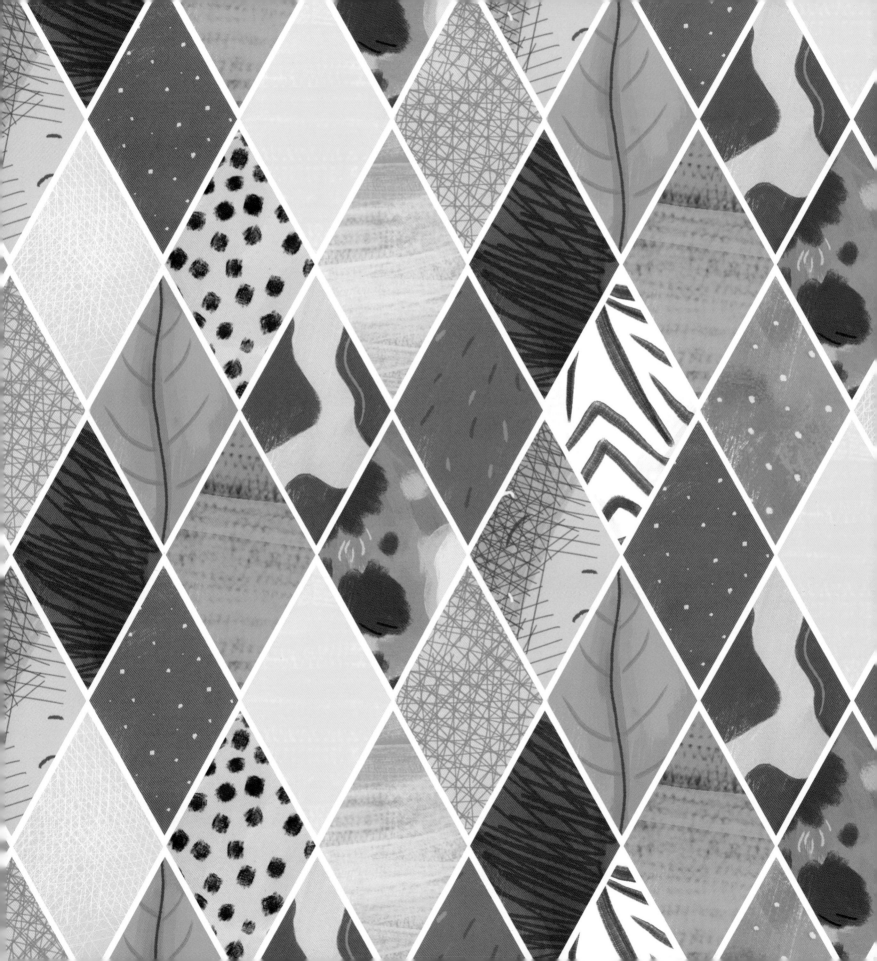